Spiders are black, but their essence is colorful.
Bring some paint and colorful thoughts into
this seemingly dark book.

Think of a positive characteristic of a spider.

A _ _ _ _ _ _ _ _ _ _

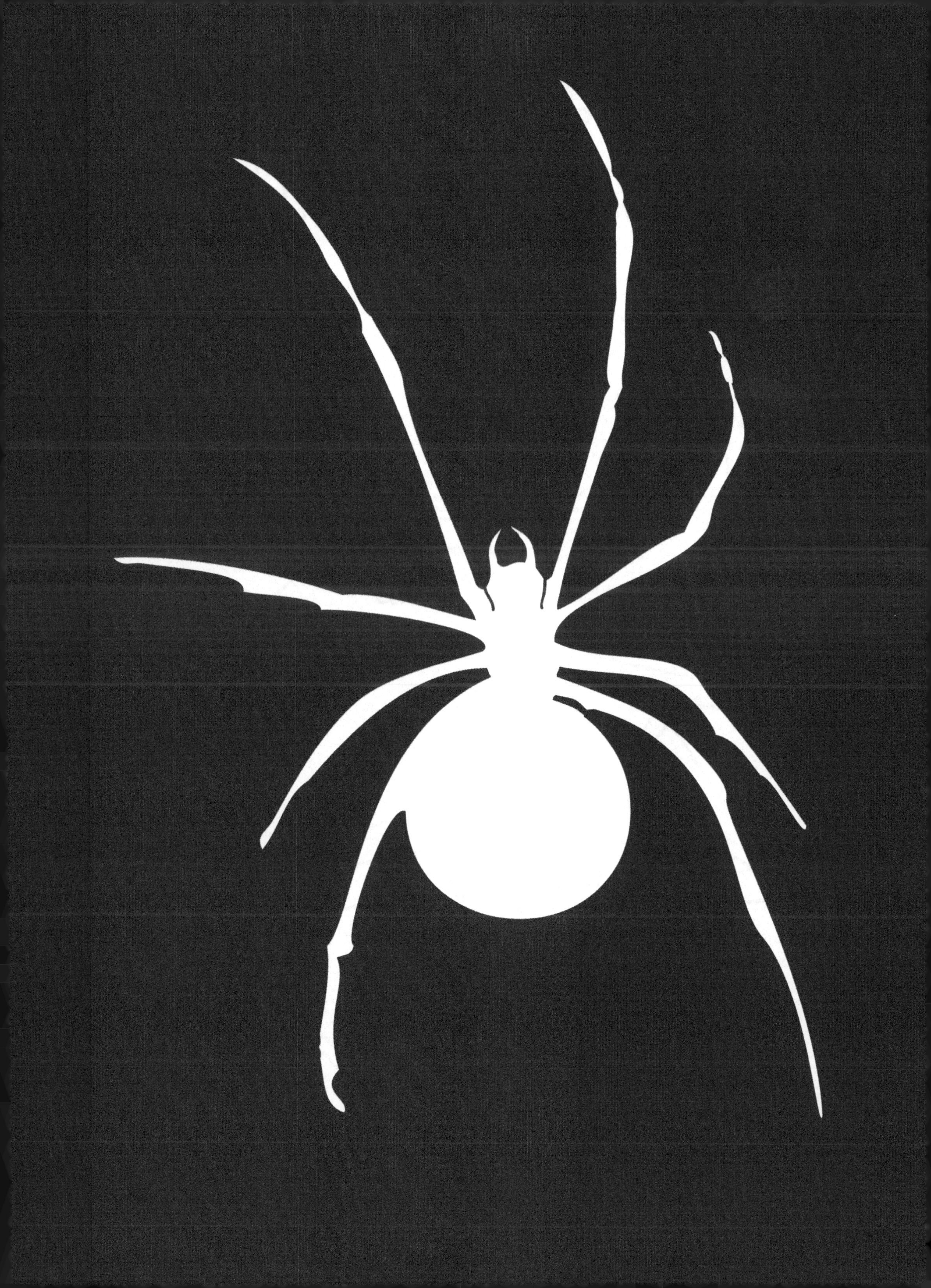

Fred the spider relaxes in a deck chair with an insect cocktail...

...paint yourself under the parasol
and keep him company.

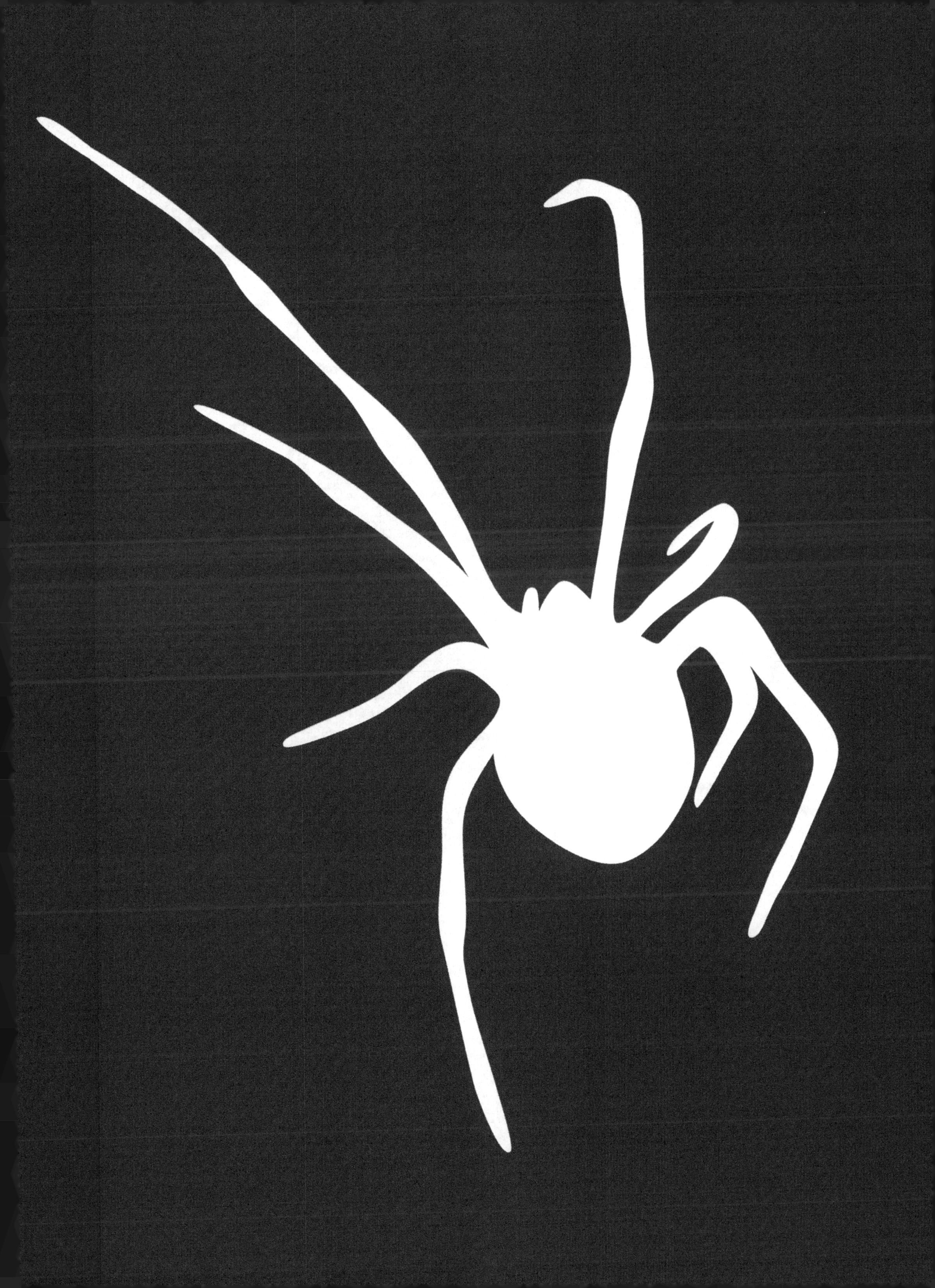

Can you help Johanna,
to catch the fly?

Wait something is missing!
Paint Fabian eight legs to get him back
for mosquito hunting again.

Paint a glass over the spider to safely transport her outside.

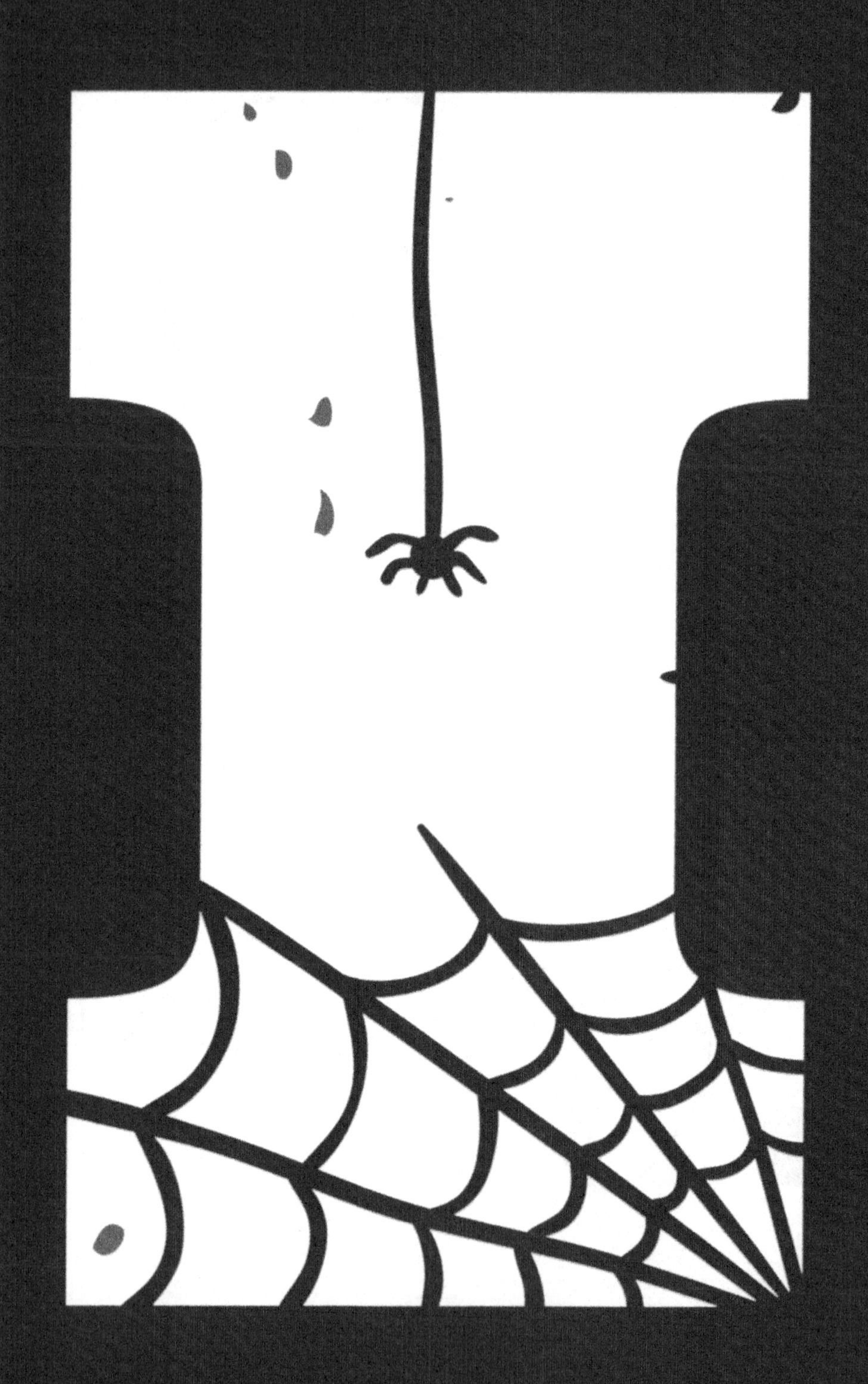

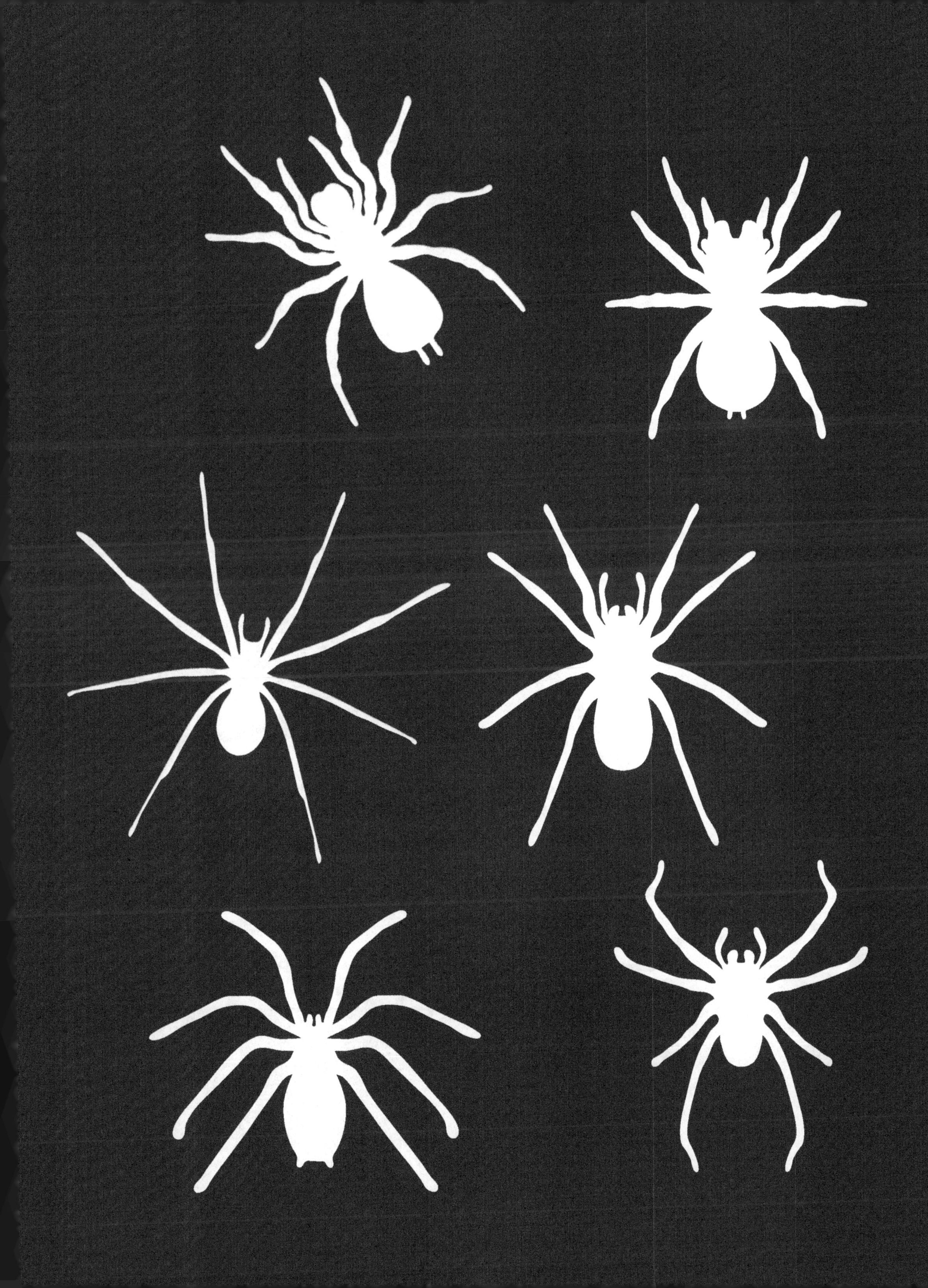

Can you help spider Carla to built her web?
Try to connect the dots.

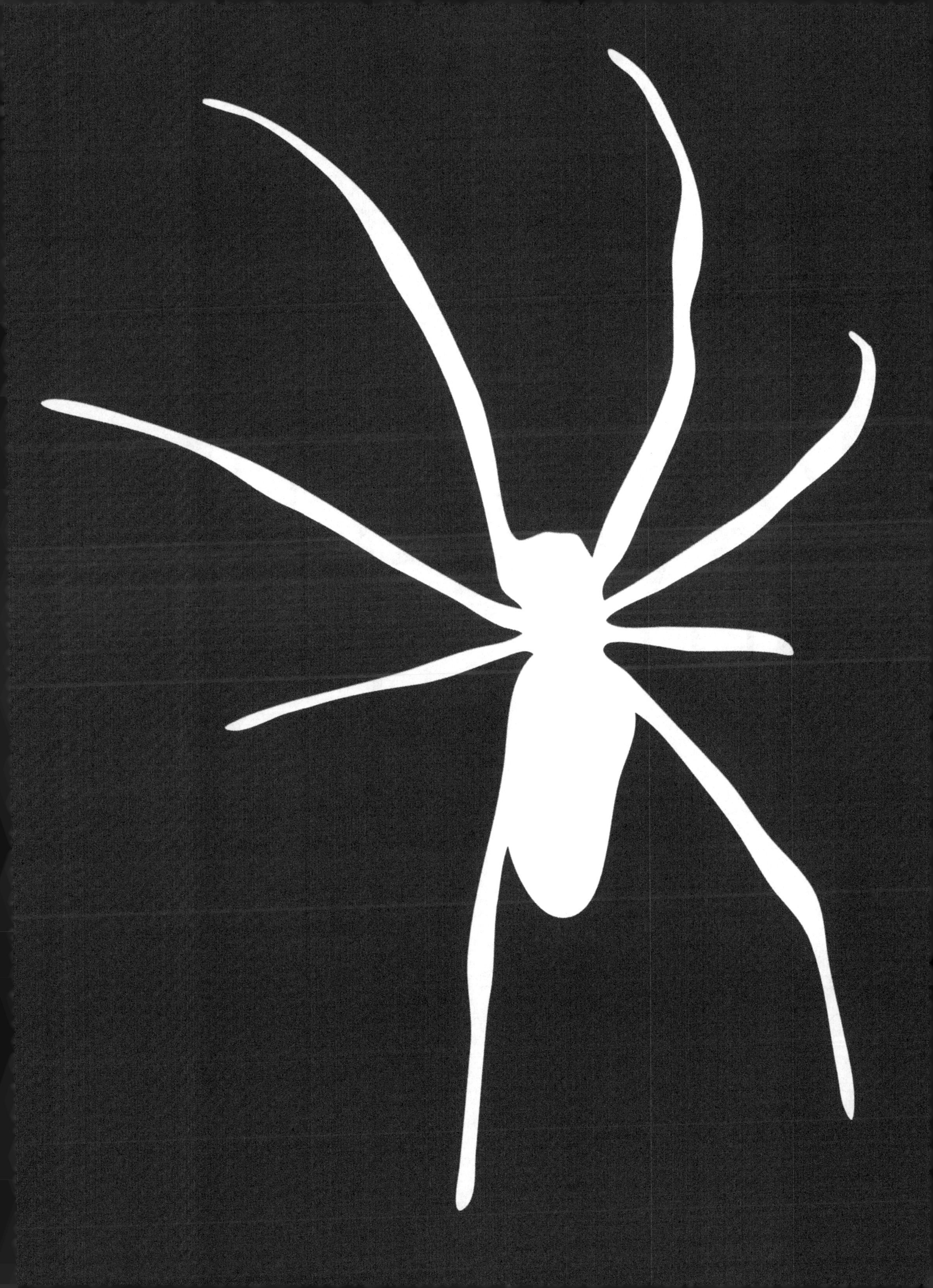

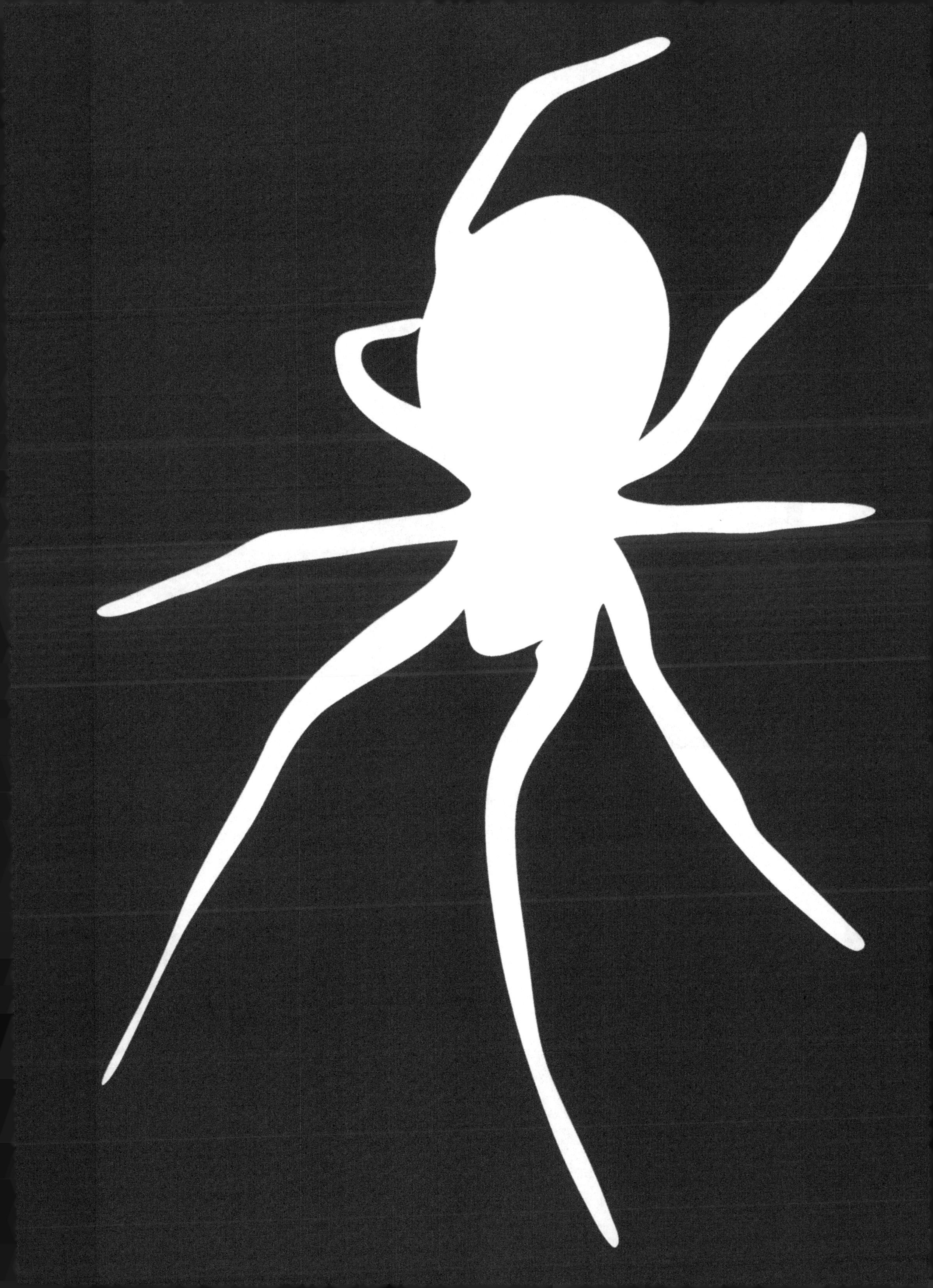

All images were purchased with the **Merch Lifetime Subscription** on vexels.com
Additionally the image "Silhouettes of spiders" Author: nikolam, from vectorstock.com (expanded license)

ISBN: 979-8-5551-2467-8

I hope you or your child enjoyed this coloring book.
My goal is to help people reduce their fear of spiders.

If you like, you can support me with a positive rating of this book.

Many thanks!

Made in the USA
Monee, IL
22 April 2022